TO
_____

FROM
_____

THE BOSS:
NAMELESS, BLAMELESS, AND SHAMELESS

A DILBERT® BOOK
BY
SCOTT ADAMS

B⬛XTREE

First published in 1998 by Andrews McMeel Publishing

This edition published in1998 by Boxtree,
an imprint of Macmillan Publishers Ltd,
25 Eccleston Place, London, SW1W 9NF and Basingstoke

Associated companies throughout the world

ISBN 0 7522 13083

9 8 7 6 5 4 3 2 1

A CIP catalogue record for this book is available from the British Library

Printed in Hong kong

THE BOSS:
NAMELESS, BLAMELESS, AND SHAMELESS

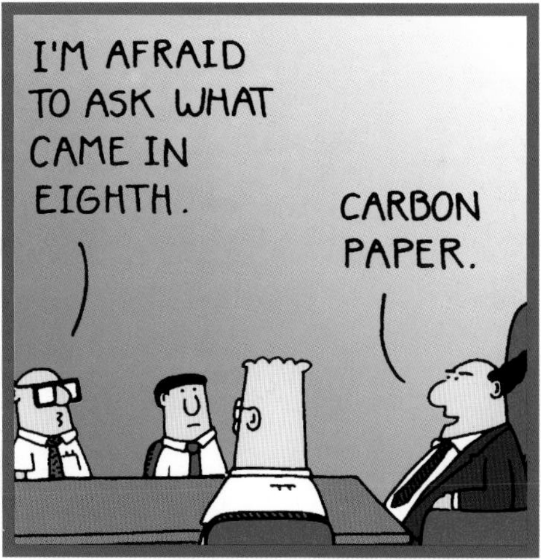
I'M AFRAID TO ASK WHAT CAME IN EIGHTH.
CARBON PAPER.

I THINK SOME RECOGNITION OF A JOB WELL-DONE IS APPROPRIATE HERE.
THANKS. IT WAS ONE OF MY BETTER EXCUSES.

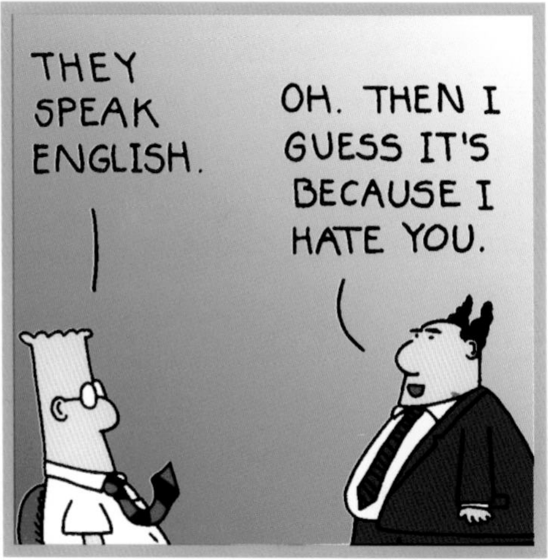
THEY SPEAK ENGLISH.
OH. THEN I GUESS IT'S BECAUSE I HATE YOU.

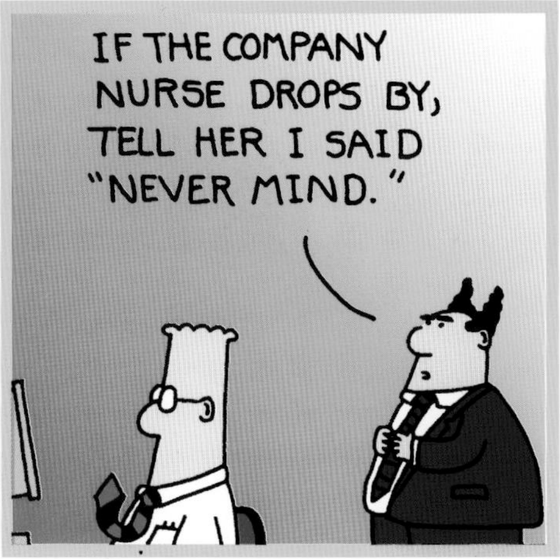
IF THE COMPANY NURSE DROPS BY, TELL HER I SAID "NEVER MIND."

SUSAN, I'M REORGANIZING THE DEPARTMENT AGAIN. THE BUDGET YOU WORKED ON FOR MONTHS IS NOW WORTHLESS.
I THINK WHEN YOU HAVE BAD NEWS YOU SHOULD MAKE AN EFFORT TO BREAK IT GRADUALLY, MAYBE BUILD UP TO IT.

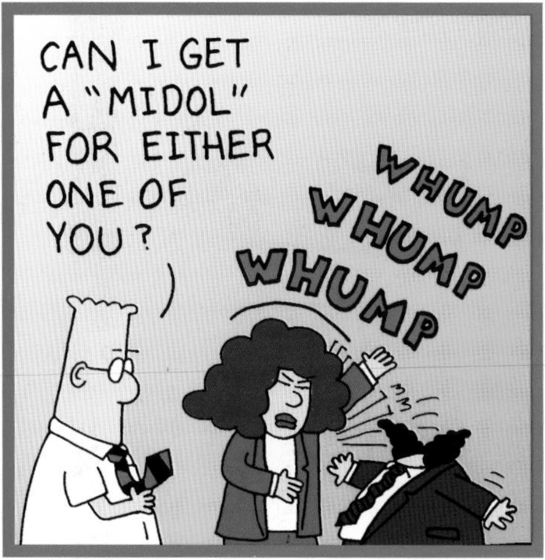
CAN I GET A "MIDOL" FOR EITHER ONE OF YOU?
WHUMP
WHUMP
WHUMP

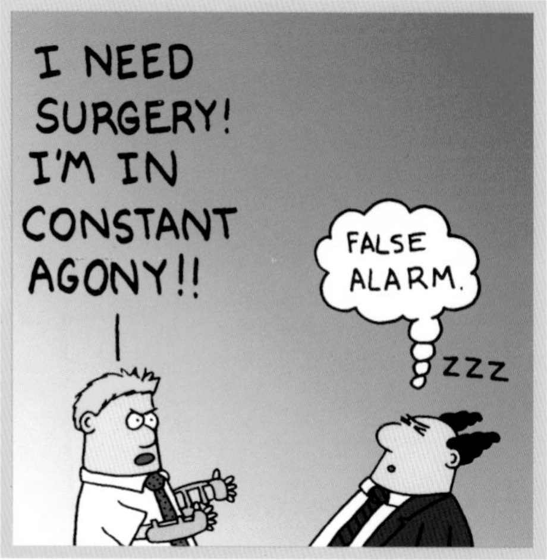
I NEED SURGERY! I'M IN CONSTANT AGONY!!
FALSE ALARM.
ZZZ

RUN AND GET ME SOME PAPER TOWELS... FIVE OF THEM... FROM THE MEN'S ROOM.
WHAP!

BAD NEWS

WE'RE NOT GIVING ANY RAISES.

MAKING IT WORSE

BUT WE THINK WORK IS ITS OWN REWARD.